营养早餐

Nutritious Breakfast

梁琼白　著

中国轻工业出版社

目 录 CONTENTS

金枪鱼土司 + 综合果汁
TUNA TOAST + ASSORTED FRESH JUICE

● 材料

　厚片全麦土司1片、金枪鱼罐头1罐、洋葱半个、蛋黄酱4大匙、黑胡椒1大匙、盐1大匙

● 作法

　1. 打开金枪鱼罐头，倒去浮油、弄碎；洋葱切碎末拌入1大匙盐，腌10分钟后挤干水分，拌入金枪鱼内，加入蛋黄酱和黑胡椒调匀。

　2. 厚片土司先烤5分钟，然后取出，铺上金枪鱼酱后抹平，放入烤箱再烤3分钟。

　3. 将烤好的土司斜角对切两半，成两片三角形。

● INGREDIENTS

1 piece thick wholewheat toast, 1 can tuna, 1/2 onion , 4T. mayonnaise, 1T. black pepper, 1T. salt

● METHODS

1. Pour away the oil of the canned tuna and mince, chop the onion and add 1T. salt, squeeze the water after marinated for 10 minutes, mix with the tuna,mayonnaise and black pepper.

2. Toast the thick toast for 5 minutes, spread the tuna mixture onto it and put into the oven for another 3 minutes.

3. Cut the toast into halves as triangle shape.

◆ 综合果汁 / ASSORTED FRESH JUICE

● 材料

　苹果2个、胡萝卜1小条、鲜橙2个、芹菜1棵

● 作法

　1. 将所有材料先洗净，再切小段或小片，放入榨汁机中榨出果汁。

　2. 滤除渣滓，盛入杯内即可饮用。

● INGREDIENTS

2 apples, 1 small carrot, 2 oranges, 1 stalk Chinese celery

● METHODS

1. Rinse all the ingredients, cut into small pieces, and add into the blender.

2. Liquidize and serve.

重点提示 NOTE

1. 金枪鱼酱可一次多做些，装在保鲜盒内随时取用。
2. 厚片土司比较好吃，但也可以随个人喜好选用不同土司。
3. 食用油一般为植物油，为烹调常用材料，在随后的"材料"介绍中不再提及。

1. Tuna mixture can be done more for one time, and put in the container for any use.
2. Thick toast is more tasty, but also can be chosen as perference.
3. Oil is vegetable oil in this book.

4

金枪鱼土司 + 综合果汁

TUNA TOAST + ASSORTED FRESH JUICE

鲜果玉米片 + 烤土司
FRESH FRUIT CEREAL + TOAST

鲜果玉米片 / FRESH FRUIT CEREAL

● 材料

新鲜草莓4个、香蕉1根、木瓜1小片、玉米片1杯、鲜奶1杯

● 作法

将各种水果洗净、去皮、切小片，放深盘内，加入玉米片，并淋入鲜奶即可食用。

● INGREDIENTS

4 strawberries, 1 banana,1 slice papaya, 1c. kellogg's cereal,1c.milk

● METHODS

Rinse and skin all kinds of fruits, cut into small pieces, put into a deep plate, add the cereal and pour the milk.Serve.

烤土司 / TOAST

● 材料

土司面包2片（鲜奶土司或全麦土司皆可）

● 作法

1. 用烤面包机或烤箱,将土司烤至两面金黄即可取出食用。

2. 可抹上奶油或果酱增加土司的口感。

● INGREDIENTS

2 pieces toasts (milk toast or wholewheat toast)

● METHODS

1. Toast the toasts golden and serve.

2. You can spread the butter or jam to emphasize the flavor.

重 点 提 示
NOTE

1. 也可以将玉米片搭配碎肉鸡汤做成咸口味食用。
2. 水果的品种没有一定限制，视个人喜爱而定。

1. It is also recommended that the minced meat chicken soup with the cereal.
2. It is up to your choice to choose the fruits, there is no restriction about this.

鲜果玉米片 + 烤土司

FRESH FRUIT CEREAL + TOAST

咸玉米片 + 水煮蛋
SALTY CORN MEAL + BOILED EGGS

● 材料
咸玉米片半杯、鲜奶1杯
● 作法
将咸玉米片放浅盘内，加入鲜奶，拌匀即可食用。

● INGREDIENTS
1/2c. salty flavored corn meal, 1c. milk
● METHODS
Pour the salty flavored corn meal into the shallow plate, also the milk and mix and serve.

水煮蛋 / BOILED EGGS

● 材料
鸡蛋2个
● 作法
1. 将鸡蛋放入煮锅内，加水没过鸡蛋，用小火煮开，水开5分钟关火，再浸泡10分钟取出。
2. 剥壳后即可食用，可蘸盐调味。

● INGREDIENTS
2 eggs
● METHODS
1. Put the eggs into the pot, add some water and cover the eggs, cook the eggs over low heat until boiling turn off the heat after 5 minutes then soaking for another 10 minutes.
2. Shell cooked eggs, dip some salt when serving.

重点提示 NOTE

可另备一些烤土司及果酱，以便食量大者可增强饱足感。

You can prepare toast and jam for those big eaters.

咸玉米片 + 水煮蛋

SALTY CORN MEAL + BOILED EGGS

9

蛋饼 + 咸豆浆
EGG PANCAKE + SALTY SOYBEANS MILK

● 材料
中筋面粉1杯、鸡蛋1个、葱2根、盐少许
● 作法
1. 将面粉放大碗内，冲入开水半杯，拌匀后加2大匙色拉油，慢慢淋入少许冷水，揉成面团，放置10分钟。

2. 将醒好的面团分5小块，每块擀成薄片，用平底锅烙成面皮。

3. 蛋打散，加入切碎的葱花及少许盐，拌匀后用少许色拉油煎，上面盖1张面皮，然后翻面，卷成筒状盛出，切斜段后盛盘即可食用。

● INGREDIENTS
1c. all-purpose flour, 1 egg, 2 scallions, a dash of salt
● METHODS
1. Pour the flour into a big bowl,add 1/2 c.boiling water, mix well and then add 2T. oil and some cold water, knead to make a dough, and place for 10 minutes.

2. Divide the dough into 5 portions, roll out into a pancake about 6 inches in diameter. Heat a frying pan, add a litte oil, fry pancake until opaque. Remove from heat.

3. Beat egg, add some chopped scallions and salt, mix well and fry the egg mixture with some oil, cover with a pancake,then flip over and roll up, cut into several pieces,then serve.

咸豆浆 / SALTY SOYBEANS MILK

● 材料
（1）黄豆300克

（2）榨菜末、油条末、葱花、虾米各少许，醋、香油、盐各少许
● 作法
1. 黄豆洗净，泡4小时，然后分次用榨汁机打碎，滤出豆浆，煮开即成原浆。

2. 碗内放入材料（2）少许，冲入煮好的原浆，调匀即成咸豆浆。

● INGREDIENTS
(1) 2/3lb. Soybeans

(2) chopped pickled vegetables, chopped crispy Chinese cruller, chopped scallions, dried shrimps, vinegar, sesame oil, salt as needed
● METHODS
1. Rinse soybeans and soak in water for 4 hours, then liquefy in a blender, remove the dregs, then bring to a boil.

2. Put the ingredients (2) into the bowl, pour the cooked soybean milk, mix and serve.

酒酿鸡蛋 + 全麦土司
RICE WINE LEES WITH EGG + WHOLEWHEAT TOAST

● 材料

　甜酒酿 2 大匙、鸡蛋 1 个、糖 2 大匙

● 作法

　1. 锅内放入 1 杯水，煮开后放糖，并加入酒酿同煮。

　2. 鸡蛋在碗内打散，淋入酒酿内煮开，关火即可盛出食用。

● INGREDIENTS

2T. rice wine lees, 1 egg, 2T. sugar

● METHODS

1. Bring 1c. water to a boil, then add sugar and rice wine lees to cook

2. Beat egg, pour in method (1) and bring to boil again, remove from heat and serve.

全麦土司 / WHOLEWHEAT TOAST

● 材料

　全麦土司 2 片

● 作法

　用烤面包机或烤箱，将土司烤至酥黄即可取出食用，可抹奶油或果酱增加风味。

● INGREDIENTS

2 pieces wholewheat toasts

● METHODS

Toast the wholewheat toasts until golden with toaster or oven,spread on the butter or jam to increase the flavor.

酒酿鸡蛋 +全麦土司

RICE WINE LEES WITH EGG + WHOLEWHEAT TOAST

13

鲜奶蒸蛋 + 小花卷
STEAMED MILK EGG + SMALL CURLY ROUND BUNS

● 材料

鲜奶2杯、鸡蛋1个、白糖2大匙

● 作法

1. 鸡蛋打散，加入鲜奶和白糖调匀，用纱网过滤后，盛在蒸碗内。盖上保鲜膜，放入电锅，外锅加水2杯，蒸至开关跳起时即可取出。

2. 撕去保鲜膜食用。

● INGREDIENTS

2c. milk, 1 egg, 2T. sugar

● METHODS

1. Beat egg, add milk and sugar, then mix well, filter egg mixture using a sifter or strainer to remove any impurities,and pour into the steaming bowl, cover with cellophane wrap and place into the rice cooker, add 2c. water in rice cooker,steam until the switch pumps and remove.

2. Remove the cellophane wrap and serve.

● 材料

现成品酌量（视各人食量）

● 作法

蒸热取出即可食用。

● INGREDIENTS

the already-made small curly round buns (depends on how much the eater can eat)

● METHODS

Steam and serve.

15

鸡丝玉米粥 + 甜馒头
SHREDDED CHICKEN AND CORN CONGEE + SWEET BUNS

鸡丝玉米粥 / SHREDDED CHICKEN AND CORN CONGEE

● 材料

鸡胸肉半块、大米1杯、玉米罐头1罐、芹菜2根、盐少许、淀粉少许

● 作法

1. 大米洗净，加水5杯煮成粥。

2. 鸡胸肉切丝，拌入少许淀粉和盐，再加入粥内同煮。

3. 加入玉米粒一同煮匀，并加少许盐调味后，关火，撒入切碎的芹菜末即成。

● INGREDIENTS

1/2 chicken breast, 1c. rice, 1 can corn, 2 sticks Chinese celery, a pinch of salt and cornstarch

● METHODS

1. Wash the rice, add 5c. water and make congee.

2. Slice the chicken breast, marinate with cornstarch and salt ,then boil together with the congee.

3. Add corn and stir well, add salt to taste, remove from heat and sprinkle with the chopped, celery ,serve.

甜馒头 / SWEET BUNS

● 材料

红糖馒头或鲜奶甜馒头

● 作法

用电锅蒸热，即可取出食用。

● INGREDIENTS

brown sugar buns or sweet milk buns

● METHODS

Steam in the rice cooker, then serve.

鸡丝玉米粥 + 甜馒头

汉堡 + 米乳
HAMBURGER + PEANUT MILK

● 材料

猪肉馅300克、洋葱半个、面包粉1杯、鲜奶1杯、姜末1茶匙、胡萝卜末1／3杯、盐1茶匙、料酒1大匙、淀粉半大匙、汉堡面包4个

● 作法

1. 先将面包粉和鲜奶调匀浸泡，再将肉馅放大碗内，加入泡软的面包粉、切碎的洋葱末和胡萝卜末、姜末等材料拌匀。

2. 加入所有调味料调好后，分成4等份小块，每块按扁后，用平底锅煎黄，再夹入汉堡面包内即可食用。可附加生菜及番茄片。

● INGREDIENTS

2/3 lb. ground pork, 1/2 onion ,chopped, 1c. bread crumbs, 1c. milk 1t. chopped ginger, 1/3c. diced carrots, 1t. salt, 1T. cooking wine, 1. 2T. cornstarch, 4 hamburger bread

● METHODS

1. Soak the bread crumbs into the milk and mix, then put ground pork into a bowl, then add the bread crumbs mixture, chopped onions and diced carrots and chopped ginger, stir well.

2. Add all the seasonings and mix well, then divide pork mixture into 4 portions, press flat each one of them. Fry in a frying pan with a little o until golden brown on both sides, then stuff in the hamburger bread Stuff in lettuce and tomato slice if desired.

◆ 米乳 / PEANUT MILK

● 材料

大米半杯、炒花生150克、糖1杯

● 作法

1. 大米洗净，泡1小时，然后加入榨汁机内，同时加水3杯将大米打碎，再倒入锅内。

2. 再加3杯水将花生打碎，一同倒入锅内同煮，并加糖调味，视黏稠状况再酌量加水调至适中稠度，即可关火盛出饮用。

● INGREDIENTS

1/2c. rice, 50z. Fried peanuts, 1c. sugar

● METHODS

1. Wash the rice and soak in water for 1 hour, then pour into the blender add 3c.water to grind, then pour into a pot .

2. Add 3c. water to smash the peanuts, then pour into the method (1 and bring to a boil, add sugar to taste, add water until it gets thickened then remove from heat and serve.

重点提示 NOTE

汉堡肉可一次多做些，再分成小块冷冻，以供随时取用。

You can make more hamburger meat at one time, divide them into small amount and freeze for any use.

19

沙拉面包盒 + 鲜果汁
SALAD BREAD + FRESH JUICE

● 材料

　　小黄瓜1条、煮熟的胡萝卜半条、熟马铃薯1个、熟鸡蛋1个、蛋黄酱半杯、土司4片、盐半大匙

● 作法

　　1. 小黄瓜洗净、切丁，加入半大匙盐腌5分钟，然后用冷开水冲净，沥干。

　　2. 将胡萝卜、马铃薯和熟鸡蛋切丁后，与小黄瓜混合，再加入蛋黄酱拌匀做成沙拉。

　　3. 将土司放平，放入少许沙拉后，盖上另一片土司，并用碗扣出圆盒状，修掉四周硬皮即成。

● INGREDIENTS

1 Chinese cucumber, 1/2 cooked carrot, 1 cooked potato, 1 boiled egg, 1/2c.

mayonnaise, 4 pieces toasts, 1/2T. salt

● METHODS

1. Wash and dice cucumber, marinate with salt for 5 minutes, then rinse under cold water. Drain.

2. Dice the cooked carrot, potato and egg, mix with cucumber dices, then add some mayonnaise to stir and make the filling.

3. Place the toast, spread some filling on top, cover with another toast, using a bowl to shape the toast as round, then cut off the rim of the toast. Ready to serve.

◆ 鲜果汁 / FRESH JUICE

● 材料

鲜橙4个

● 作法

鲜橙洗净，对剖两半，榨出果汁即可饮用。

● INGREDIENTS

4 oranges

● METHODS

Clean the oranges and halve, then squeeze them into juice.

重点提示
NOTE

没有鲜橙的季节，可用其他水果代替，或改用盒装果汁。

If the oranges are not in season,you can also replace with other fruits, or use package juice.

沙拉面包盒 +鲜果汁

鱼汤煨面
FISH SOUP NOODLES

● 材料

　鲷鱼片 1 包（约 225 克）、雪里蕻 75 克、高汤 3 杯、盐 1 茶匙、细拉面 150 克

● 作法

　1. 鲷鱼片洗净、切片，雪里蕻洗好、切碎，高汤先放锅内，烧开后加入鱼片和雪里蕻同煮，并加盐调味。

　2. 水半锅烧开，放入细拉面煮熟，捞入高汤锅内，与汤料同煮，约 5 分钟，即可关火盛出食用。

● INGREDIENTS

1 bag bream slices (1/2lb.),3oz.
preserved mustard green ,3c.stock, 1t. salt, 5oz. thin noodles

● METHODS

1. Clean and slice the bream, wash and chop preserved mustard green; put the stock into a pot ,bring to a boil, add the breams and mustard green to cook, then add salt to taste.
2. Bring half pot of water to a boil. add noodles to cook until done, then remove and cook with the stock for 5 minutes, remove from heat and ready to serve.

清粥 + 小菜
CONGEE + SIDE DISHES

● 材料

大米 1 杯

● 作法

1. 大米洗净，加水 5 杯浸泡 20 分钟后，移至炉上煮开。

2. 改小火熬煮至米粒黏稠即可关火盛出。

● INGREDIENTS

1c. rice

● METHODS

1. Rinse the rice, soak in 5c. water for 20 minutes, then bring to a boil.

2. Keep simmering with over low heat, cook until the rice gets thickened. Serve.

◆ 小菜 / SIDE DISHES

● 作法

卤牛肉

牛腱汆烫去掉血水，另以清水煮半小时，然后加入八角五香包，再加适量的料酒、酱油、糖，卤入味后再切细条，淋少许卤汁即成。

小鱼干

小银鱼 75 克先用清水泡 10 分钟，然后沥干，锅内用 3 大匙油炒香葱、姜末，再放入小鱼干煸炒，最后加入辣椒同炒，并淋入少许酱油、胡椒粉及一点糖调味，炒匀即盛出。

菜脯蛋

萝卜干 40 克洗净、切碎，加 2 瓣大蒜(切成末)同炒，然后盛出放凉。另将鸡蛋 2 个打散，拌入萝卜干，然后用平底锅煎成小蛋片，两面煎黄即盛出。

● METHODS

Stewed Beef

Blanch the beef first, cook in water for 30 minutes, then add some star anises and five-spice bag, season with wine, soy sauce, sugar. cook until the flavor is absorbed slice and pour some sauce on it, then serve.

Dried Small Fish

Soak 3oz.dried salted whitebaits in water for 10 minutes, drain. Stir-fry the chopped scallions and ginger with 3T. oil until fragrant, add white-baits to stir-fry until dry, then add chili peppers, soy sauce, pepper, and a bit of sugar to taste, stir well and serve.

Egg with Preserved Chinese Radish

Clean and chop 1 oz. Preserved Chinese radish. stir-fry together with 2 cloves garlic (chopped), then remove and set aside. Beat 2 eggs mix with the stir-fried preserved Chinese radish, then fry as the pan-cake shape until golden, then ready to serve.

茶泡饭 / RICE IN TEA

- ● **材料**

  白饭半碗、热乌龙茶1杯
- ● **作法**

  将白饭盛入碗内，冲入乌龙茶，拌匀即可食用。

- ● INGREDIENTS

  1/2 bowl cooked rice, 1c. hot Oolong tea
- ● METHODS

  Put the rice in the bowl, pour the hot Oolong tea, mix together and serve.

◆ 小菜 / SIDE DISHES

- ● **作法**

卤牛肚

牛肚先煮烂，再加五香包和酱油同卤入味，再切条食用（可买现成品）。

卤花生

花生洗净，先煮熟，再加八角、少许盐卤入味即可。

卤豆干

五香豆干放入卤汤中卤入味，再取出切条食用；没有卤汤者，可用高汤加酱油、八角烧入味即可。

- ● METHODS

Stewed Beef Tripe

Cook the beef tripe until soft, then add the five-spice bag and soy sauce to taste, and cook until the flavor is absorbed, slice when serving this dish.

Stewed Peanuts

Clean the peanuts, cook until done, then add the star anises and some salt to taste, cook until the flavor is absorbed.

Stewed Pressed Tofu

Place five-flavored pressed tofu into stewing sauce and cook until the flavor is absorbed, then slice when eating. If you don't prepare the stewing sauce at home, it is suggested that using the stock together with soy sauce and star anises, and stew to flavored.

重点提示 NOTE

1. 以冷饭泡热茶或冷茶泡热饭方式，能尝到茶泡饭的风味。
2. 以上小菜没有内容限制，随各人口味搭配即可。

1. Hot tea or cold tea if desired.
2. There is no restriction of the dishes, you can choose whatever you like to taste.

绿豆粥 + 炸馒头片
MUNG BEAN CONGEE + FRIED BUNS

● 材料

绿豆 1 杯、大米 2 杯

● 作法

1. 绿豆洗净，泡水 1 小时；大米洗净，泡水 20 分钟。

2. 将绿豆和大米一同放入锅内，加入适量清水，先煮开，再改小火，熬煮至绿豆和米粒皆已软烂即成。

● INGREDIENTS

1c. mung beans, 2c.rice

● METHODS

1. Rinse the mung beans, soak in water for 1 hour. Rinse the rice and soak in water for 20 minutes.

2. Put the mung beans and rice altogether into the pot, add enough water, and bring to a boil, then reduce heat to low ,cook until the mung beans and rice get softened. Serve.

炸馒头片 / FRIED BUNS

● 材料

馒头 1 个(冰过)、盐 1 茶匙

● 作法

1. 先将盐放大碗内，加水 1 杯调匀成盐水。

2. 冷馒头切厚片，锅内放油 2 杯先烧热，再将馒头片——沾盐水后，立刻放入热油中，炸至两面金黄即可盛出。

● INGREDIENTS

1 frozen San Don bun, 1t. salt

● METHODS

1. Place the salt into a big bowl, add 1c. water and mix to salty water.

2. Slice bun. Heat 2c. oil, then dip the buns into salty water then put into the hot oil immediately, deep-fry until golden brown on both sides, then serve.

重点提示 NOTE

泡过盐水的馒头片不会吸油，外酥里嫩。

The buns soaked in salty water won't be greasy, and crispy outside and soft inside.

韭菜盒 + 小米粥
CHINESE CHIVE CAKE + MILLET CONGEE

● 材料

中筋面粉 2 杯、韭菜 150 克、粉丝 1 把、盐适量、香油少许

● 作法

1. 将中筋面粉放盆内，加入开水 2/3 杯、冷水 1/3 杯，并加少许盐，揉匀成面团，盖上湿布醒 20 分钟。

2. 韭菜洗净、切碎，粉丝泡软、切碎，两者混合后，加少许盐和香油调味，做成馅。

3. 将面团分小块，每块包入韭菜馅料少许，捏成包子状，再按扁，放入平底锅，用少量油煎至两面金黄即可盛出食用。

● INGREDIENTS

2c. all purpose flour, 5oz. Chinese chive, 1bunch mung bean noodles, a pinch of salt, dash of sesame oil

● METHODS

1. Place flour in the pot ,pour in 2/3c. boiling water and 1/3c. cold water, add a bit of salt, knead to make a dough, then cover a wet cloth and set for 20 minutes.

2. Rinse and chop Chinese chive; soften the mung bean noodles in water, chop, mix the two kinds together, add salt and sesame oil to taste and make the filling.

3. Divide the dough into small pieces, stuff the Chinese chive filling into each small dough ,and shape them as a bun ,press flat ,then fry with a little oil in fry pan ,cook until golden on both sides, then serve.

 小米粥 / MILLET CONGEE

● 材料

小米 1 杯、碎玉米 1/3 杯

● 作法

1. 小米洗净，加入碎玉米拌匀，一同加水 7 杯浸泡半小时。

2. 移至火上烧开，改小火，煮至米粒软烂黏稠时，即可关火，放凉食用。

● INGREDIENTS

1c. millet, 1/3c. cracked corn

● METHODS

1. Wash the millet and mix with the cracked corn, soak in 7c.water for 30 minutes.

2. Bring method (1) to a boil, then reduce heat to low, cook until the millet and cracked corn soften ,remove from heat, let cool, serve.

新月牛肉包 + 鸡蛋鲜奶
BEEF CROISSANT + EGG MILK

● 材料

　新月形面包、卤牛肉、生菜、番茄各适量

● 作法

　1. 新月形面包先用利刀在弯角内侧划开刀口，放入烤箱烤至香酥时取出。

　2. 卤牛肉切片，生菜洗净、切丝，番茄切薄片。

　3. 将每个新月形面包的切口打开，放入卤牛肉和生菜丝及番茄片各少许，夹紧即可食用。

● INGREDIENTS

croissant, stewed beef, lettuce, tomato as needed

● METHODS

1. Cut the inside layer of the croissant, then place it into the oven, bake until crispy, remove and set aside.

2. slice stewed beef; wash and shred lettuce; slice tomato thinly.

3. Pull the croissant open, and stuff in the stewed beef, shredded lettuce, and the tomato slice, press them tightly and ready to serve.

 鸡蛋鲜奶 / EGG MILK

● 材料

　鸡蛋1个、鲜奶3/4杯、糖2大匙

● 作法

　鸡蛋打散，加入鲜奶和糖调匀，用纱网过滤后，盛入深碗内，盖上保鲜膜，放入电锅，外锅加水1杯，蒸至开关跳起，即可取出食用。

● INGREDIENTS

1 egg, 3/4c.milk, 2T.sugar

● METHODS

Beat egg, add milk and sugar, stir well, filter egg mixture using a sifter, pour into a deep bowl, cover with a cellophane wrap, and put it into the rice cooker, add water on the outside rim of the rice cooker, steam until the button jumps up, ready to serve.

新月牛肉包 + 鸡蛋鲜奶

BEEF CROISSANT + EGG MILK

煎饭饼 + 薏仁绿豆汤
RICE PANCAKE + PEARL BARLEY AND MUNG BEAN SOUP

····· 煎饭饼 / RICE PANCAKE ◆

● 材料

白饭 1 碗、鸡蛋 1 个、鲜奶半杯、盐半茶匙

● 作法

1. 白饭与牛奶先拌匀，浸泡 10 分钟，再将鸡蛋打入，拌匀，加盐调味。

2. 用平底锅加少许油烧热，再将调好的饭盛少许放在平底锅上，小火煎至两面金黄即可盛出。

● INGREDIENTS

1 bowl cooked rice, 1 egg, 1/2c. milk, 1/2t. salt

● METHODS

1. Mix cooked rice and milk well, soak for 10 minutes, add the egg, stir well, then add salt to taste.

2. Heat a little oil in a fryer pan, fry some rice mixture with over low heat until golden brown on both sides. Ready to serve.

◆ 薏仁绿豆汤 / PEARL BARLEY AND MUNG BEAN SOUP ·····

● 材料

薏仁 75 克、绿豆 300 克、糖 300 克

● 作法

1. 薏仁洗净，先泡水 1 小时，再加水盖过，放入电锅先蒸熟，外锅加水 2 杯，蒸至开关跳起后取出。

2. 绿豆洗净，泡水 1 小时后，放火上，加水 10 杯煮至绿豆裂开时，放入薏仁同煮，待两者皆已熟烂，即加糖调味，煮匀即可关火盛出食用。

● INGREDIENTS

3oz. Pearl barley, 2/3lb. mung beans, 2/3lb. sugar

● METHODS

1. Wash pearl barley, soak in water for 1 hour, add some water to cover the pearl barley, steam in rice cooker, add 2c. water on the outside rim of the rice cooker, remove until the button jumps up.

2. Wash the mung beans, soak in water for 1 hour, add 10c. water, cook until the mung beans soft, add the pearl barley together and boil until both get softened, add sugar to taste, mix well, remove from heat and ready to serve.

重点提示 NOTE

薏仁绿豆汤冷热食皆可。

Hot mung bean soup or cold mung bean soup is both OK!

起士土司 + 蔬果汁
CHEESE TOAST + VEGETABLE AND FRUIT JUICE

● 材料

　　白土司 2 片、西式火腿 2 片、方形起司片 2 片

● 作法

　　白土司修除四周硬边，两片土司中间放入起司片和西式火腿片，压紧，用利刀斜角切成三角形即成。

● INGREDIENTS

2 pieces toasts, 2 slices ham, 2 pieces square cheese

● METHODS

Cut the rim of the toasts, place the cheese and ham in the middle cover another toast, press tightly, using a sharp knife to halve as the triangle shape, and ready to serve.

蔬果汁 / VEGETABLE AND FRUIT JUICE

● 材料

　　芹菜 1 根、圆白菜 1 小块、胡萝卜 1 根、番茄 1 个、糖 4 大匙

● 作法

　　芹菜洗净、切小段，圆白菜洗净、切碎，胡萝卜切小片，番茄切片。所有材料一同放入榨汁机内打碎，滤出汁液，再加糖调味即可饮用。

● INGREDIENTS

1 stalk Chinese celery, 1 piece green cabbage, 1 carrot, 1 tomato, 4T sugar

● METHODS

Wash celery and cut into small pieces; wash green cabbage, chop slice carrot and tomato thinly. Blend all ingredients in a blender, filter mixture using a sifter, and add sugar to taste, ready to serve.

松饼 + 奶茶
PANCAKE + MILK TEA

● 材料

　　低筋面粉 1 杯、鸡蛋 1 个、鲜奶半杯、糖 2 大匙、泡打粉 1 大匙

● 作法

　　1．将所有材料拌匀，成浓糊状，将平底锅烧热，用少许奶油涂抹锅内，再舀入少许面糊，小火烘至两面金黄即可盛出。

　　2．食用时，可抹果酱，也可用奶油调味。

● INGREDIENTS

1c. cake flour, 1 egg, 1/2c. milk, 2T. sugar, 1T. baking powder

● METHODS

1. Mix all the ingredients, and make it as a batter. Heat up the fryer pan, grease butter in the pan ,then pour some batter in ,and fry over low heat until golden brown on both sides,then ready to serve.

2. Coating some jam when serving, also you can flavor with butter.

奶茶 / MILK TEA

● 材料

　　红茶 2 大匙、鲜奶半杯、糖 3 大匙

● 作法

　　1．将红茶放煮锅内，加水 1 杯半煮开，改小火煮 10 分钟，再加入鲜奶和糖煮匀。

　　2．用纱网滤去茶叶，盛入杯内即可饮用。

● INGREDIENTS

2T. dried black tea leaves, 1/2c. milk, 3T. sugar

● METHODS

1. Put the black tea leaves in a pot ,add 11/2c. water and bring to a boil then reduce heat to low and cook for 10 minutes, then add milk and sugar to mix well.

2. Liquidize the black tea with muslin, then pour into the cup, and ready to serve.

松饼₊奶茶

肉松卷 / DRIED FRIED PORK ROLL

● 材料

千层饼 2 块、肉松 4 大匙、蛋黄 1 个

● 作法

1. 将千层饼摊开，铺上肉松 2 大匙，然后卷成筒状，另将蛋黄打散，加 2 大匙水调匀，用刷子刷一层在千层饼上。另一张千层饼同样作法。

2. 放入烤箱，以 200℃烤 10 分钟，待外皮酥黄，即可取出食用。

● INGREDIENTS

2 frozen puff pastry, 4T. dried fried pork, 1 egg yolk

● METHODS

1. Roll the puff pastry flat, sprinkle 2T. dried fried pork, then roll up. Beat egg yolk, mix with 2T. water, and brush one layer onto the flat pastry.

2. Put into the oven, bake with 200℃ for 10 minutes, wait until the pastry is crispy, then ready to serve.

玉米汤 / CORN SOUP

● 材料

玉米酱半罐、鸡蛋 1 个、水淀粉 3 大匙、盐半茶匙

● 作法

1. 玉米酱打开，放锅内，加水 2 杯煮开，加盐调味，再慢慢淋入水淀粉，勾芡成黏稠状。

2. 鸡蛋打散，加水 1 大匙再打匀，慢慢淋入玉米汤内，待蛋花浮起时即关火，盛出食用。

● INGREDIENTS

1/2 can corn paste, 1 egg, 3T. cornstarch solution, 1/2t. salt

● METHODS

1. Bring corn paste and 2c. water to a boil, add salt to taste, then thicken with cornstarch solution.

2. Beat egg, add 1T. water then mix well, pour the egg mixture slowly into the corn soup, remove from heat until the egg floats up, then ready to serve.

肉松卷 + 玉米汤

DRIED FRIED PORK ROLL + CORN SOUP

冬菜粉丝汤 + 荷包蛋

PRESERVED VEGETABLE AND MUNG BEAN NOODLES SOUP + FRIED EGG

冬菜粉丝汤 / PRESERVED VEGETABLE AND MUNG BEAN NOODLES SOUP

- **材料**

  粉丝1把、冬菜2大匙、高汤2杯、盐1/4茶匙、香菜少许

- **作法**

  1. 粉丝用冷水泡软，切两段。锅内先放高汤，再加入洗净的冬菜煮开。

  2. 放入粉丝同煮，并加盐调味，煮软即关火，最后撒入香菜末即成。

- **INGREDIENTS**

  1 bundle mung bean noodles, 2T. preserved vegetable, 2c.stock, 1/4t . salt, coriander as needed

- **METHODS**

  1. Soften the mung bean noodles in cold water, cut into halves. Bring stock and cleaned preserved vegetable to a boil.

  2. Add the mung bean noodles in and cook together, add salt to taste cook until soft and remove from heat. Sprinkle some chopped coriander and ready to serve.

荷包蛋 / FRIED EGG

- **材料**

  鸡蛋2个、盐少许

- **作法**

  平底锅烧热，放少许油，再将鸡蛋直接打入锅内，同时加少许盐，小火煎至微黄时，翻面对折，煎好即盛出。食用时可淋少许酱油调味。

- **INGREDIENTS**

  2 eggs, a pinch of salt

- **METHODS**

  Heat a fryer pan ,put a bit of oil in ,get the egg straight into the pan add a little bit of salt, fry the egg over low heat with golden brown slightly, turn it over and fold, then ready to serve, It is suggested that you can flavor with soy sauce when serving.

冬菜粉丝汤 + 荷包蛋

PRESERVED VEGETABLE AND MUNG BEAN NOODLES SOUP + FRIED EGG

简便锅贴 + 豆浆
FRIED DUMPLINGS + SOYBEAN MILK

● 材料

饺子皮10张、肉馅150克、葱末1大匙、姜汁1大匙、料酒半大匙、淀粉半茶匙

● 作法

1. 将肉馅再剁细，然后拌人葱末、姜汁、料酒和淀粉调匀。

2. 每张饺子皮包入馅料少许，然后对折捏成长条形，放入平底锅用少许油煎至两面金黄，即可盛出食用(记住加半杯面粉水，加盖焖，汤汁收干即可盛出)。

● INGREDIENTS

10 dumpling wrappers, 5oz. ground pork, 1T. copped scallions, 1T. ginger juice, 1/2T. cooking wine, 1/2t. cornstarch

● METHODS

1. Chop ground pork finely, then add the chopped scallions, ginger juice, wine and cornstarch together and mix well to make filling.

2. Stuff the filling into each dumpling wrapper, then fold it like strip shape. Fry with a little oil in the fryer pan and cook until golden brown on both sides, then ready to serve.(Be sure to remember to add 1/2c flour solution, simmering with cover on, after the sauce is gettin dry then ready to serve.)

豆浆 / SOYBEAN MILK

● 材料

黄豆300克，糖1杯

● 作法

黄豆洗净，用水浸泡4小时，然后用榨汁机打碎，沥出浆汁后，煮开，加糖调味即可盛出饮用。

● INGREDIENTS

2/3lb. soybeans, 1c. sugar

● METHODS

Wash the soybeans, soak in water for 4 hours, then put into the blender, liquidize and bring to a boil, add sugar to taste and ready to serve.

重 点 提 示
N OTE

豆浆亦可买现成的。

You can also choose the already-made Soybean Milk.

鲑鱼饭 + 蔬菜清汤
SALMON RICE + VEGETABLE SOUP

● 材料

鲑鱼1片(约225克)、大米2杯、盐半茶匙、料酒少许

● 作法

1. 鲑鱼洗净，抹少许料酒，放入烤箱以250℃烤15分钟，微黄时即取出，将鱼皮、鱼骨剔除，鱼肉弄碎。

2. 大米洗净，加水2杯浸泡10分钟，然后煮成饭，趁热取出与鱼肉拌和均匀，并加盐调味。

3. 将饭锅移至炉上，小火烘焙至水分完全消失即可关火盛出。

● INGREDIENTS

1 salmon fillet (1/2lb.), 2c. rice, 1/2t. salt, dash of cooking wine

● METHODS

1. Wash the salmon, rub on a bit of wine, bake in the oven on 250°Ê for 15minutes, remove when it becomes golden, discard the bones and skin, chop.

2. Wash the rice, add 2c. water and soak for 10 minutes, then cook until done, mix with the chopped salmon while hot, and add salt to taste.

3. Move the rice to the stove, keep cooking with over low heat until the water goes dry, remove from heat and ready to serve.

蔬菜清汤 / VEGETABLE SOUP

● 材料

小白菜2棵、番茄1个、豆腐1小块、盐1茶匙

● 作法

1. 小白菜洗净、切小段，番茄洗净、切片，豆腐切小块。

2. 锅内放3杯水烧开，先放豆腐和番茄煮开，再改小火煮5分钟，加盐调味，最后放小白菜，煮熟即关火盛出。

● INGREDIENTS

2 stalks baby Chinese cabbage,1 tomato, 1 cake tofu, 1t. salt

● METHODS

1. Wash Chinese cabbage, cut into small sections; wash and slice the tomato, and cut tofu into small pieces.

2. Boil 3c. water, add the tofu and tomato and bring to a boil, then reduce heat to low and cook for 5 minutes, add salt to taste, put the Chinese cabbage at the last minute, cook until done, remove from heat, and ready to serve.

鲑鱼饭 + 蔬菜清汤

SALMON RICE + VEGETABLE SOUP

鸡肉馄饨汤 + 干拌面
CHICKEN WONTON SOUP + MIXING NOODLES

● 材料

鸡胸肉 1 块、蛋白 2 个、料酒 1 大匙、盐半茶匙、胡椒粉少许、淀粉半匙、馄饨皮 75 克、小白菜 1 棵、高汤 2 杯

● 作法

1. 鸡胸肉去皮、洗净、剁碎，加入蛋白拌匀，再调入料酒、盐、胡椒粉和淀粉调味，做成肉馅。

2. 每张馄饨皮包入肉馅少许，捏紧成馄饨状，放入开水中煮至浮起。

3. 高汤烧开，加少许盐调味，将小白菜洗净、切小段、烫熟，再盛入馄饨碗中即成。

● INGREDIENTS

1 chicken breast, 2 egg whites, 1T. cooking wine, 1/2t. salt, pinch o pepper, 1/2t. cornstarch, 3oz. wonton wrappers, 1 stalk baby Chinese cabbage, 2c. stock

● METHODS

1. Skin, wash and chop chicken breast, add egg whites and mix well then add wine, salt, pepper and cornstarch to taste, then make the filling.

2. Stuff the filling into each wonton wrapper, and make it the wonton shape, then put into the boiling water and wait until floating up.

3. Boil the stock, and add with a bit of salt to tast. Then add cleaned and sectioned Chinese cabbage to cook until done, then add the wonton ,ready to serve.

干拌面 / MIXING NOODLES

● 材料

细拉面酌量、葱花半大匙、酱油 1 大匙、黑醋半大匙、猪油 1 大匙

● 作法

1. 水半锅烧开，放入细拉面煮熟。

2. 碗内先加调味料调匀，再放入细拉面拌匀，最后撒葱花即成。

● INGREDIENTS

thin noodles as needed, 1/2T. chopped scallions, 1T. soy sauce, 1/2T black vinegar, 1T. lard

● METHODS

1. Boil holf pot of water, add the noodles and cook until done, drain.

2. Add all seasonings in the bowl first, mix well, then put the noodles later, stir well,then sprinkle on the chopped scallions, then ready to serve.

南瓜饼 + 蔬菜粥
PUMPKIN CAKE + VEGETABLE CONGEE

● 材料

南瓜半个(约600克)、葱2根、中筋面粉1杯、盐半茶匙

● 作法

1. 南瓜去皮，洗净后刨成丝，放大碗内，再加入切好的葱花、油、面粉、盐和半杯清水调成面糊。

2. 平底锅烧热，加少许油，舀少许面糊，以小火煎成饼，两面微黄时即可盛出。

● INGREDIENTS

1/2 pumpkin (11/3lb.), 2 scallions, chopped, 1c. all purpose flour, 1/2t. salt

● METHODS

1. Skin, wash and shred the pumpkin, then place into a big bowl, add the chopped scallions, oil, salt and water to make the batter.

2. Heat a fryer pan ,add a bit of oil, and pour some batter in and fry with over low heat until golden brown slightly, then ready to serve.

● 材料

大米1杯、冷冻三色蔬菜2杯、盐半茶匙

● 作法

大米洗净，加水5杯煮成粥，米粒半熟时加入三色蔬菜同煮，待米粒熟烂成粥时，加盐调味，即可盛出食用。

● INGREDIENTS

1c. rice, 2c. frozen assorted vegetable, 1/2t. salt

● METHODS

Wash the rice, add 5c. water to cook congee, add the vegetables and boil together while the rice is half cooked,after the rice is wholy cooked as a congee, add salt to taste, and ready to serve.

南瓜饼 + 蔬菜粥

PUMPKIN CAKE + VEGETABLE CONGEE

麦片牛奶 + 烤薯球
CEREAL MILK + BAKED POTATO BALL

● 材料

即食麦片 3 大匙、鲜奶 1 杯半

● 作法

先将牛奶微微加温，关火后倒入即食麦片，盛碗内即可食用。

● INGREDIENTS

3T. instant cereal, 11/2c.milk

● METHODS

Warm up the milk, remove from heat and quickly pour into the instant cereal, mix well and ready to serve.

烤薯球 / BAKED POTATO BALL

● 材料

马铃薯 2 小个、起士丝半杯、铝箔纸 2 张

● 作法

1. 马铃薯去皮、洗净，先在微波炉内加热 10 分钟，然后装入铝箔纸折成的小盒内。

2. 用叉子在马铃薯上戳小洞，上面撒入起士丝，移入烤箱，以 250℃烤 10 分钟，待上面酥黄时，即可取出食用。

● INGREDIENTS

2 potatoes, 1/2c. grated cheese, 2 sheets aluminum foil

● METHODS

1. Skin the potatoes, rinse and microwave the potatoes for 10 minutes then place into the box with aluminum foil wrapped around.

2. Use the fork to scratch the potatoes, then sprinkle the grated cheese on, move into the oven and bake with 250℃ for 10 minutes wait until the potatoes are crispy and golden, then ready to serve.

+烤薯球

CEREAL MILK + BAKED POTATO BALL

翡翠面片汤
SPINACH PASTRY SOUP

● 材料

　　中筋面粉2杯、鸡蛋1个、菠菜150克、盐半茶匙、高汤3杯、葱1根

● 作法

　　1. 面粉放盆内，另将菠菜洗净、切碎，加水1杯打成泥，再将菜汁沥出，拌入面粉内，并将鸡蛋打散加入。加盐调味，全部揉匀成面团，然后盖上湿布醒10分钟。

　　2. 水半锅烧开，将揉好的面团用手撕成小片，放入煮熟。

　　3. 汤碗内盛入高汤，并加盐调味后，捞入煮好的面片，并撒入切碎的葱花即成。

● INGREDIENTS

2c.all purpose flour, 1 egg, 5oz. Spinach, 1/2t. salt, 3c. stock, 1 scallion, chopped

● METHODS

1. Place the flour into a mixing bowl. Wash and chop the spinach, add 1c. water and smash in the blender, then liquidize the juice, mix with the flour, then add beaten egg and salt, knead to make a dough finely, cover on wet cloth for 10 minutes.

2. Boil half pot of water, tear the dough into small pieces by hand and put into the pot and cook until done.

3. Have some boiling stock in the bowl, flavor with some salt, add the cooked pastry, and sprinkle the chopped scallions. Ready to serve.

牛肉葱饼卷 / BEEF ROLL

● 材料

　　冷冻葱油饼 2 张、卤牛肉 8 片、甜面酱 3 大匙、糖 1 大匙

● 作法

　　1．平底锅内放少许油，将葱油饼放人，小火煎至两面金黄时盛出。

　　2．煎好的葱油饼摊平，先抹一层炒好的甜面酱，再铺人 4 片卤牛肉，然后卷成筒状，食用时先用刀斜切两刀成三小段即可。

● INGREDIENTS

2 pieces frozen Chinese pancake, 8 slices stewed beef

● METHODS

1. Fry Chinese pancake with a bit of oil with over low heat until golden brown on both sides.

2. Flat the pancake, spread one layer with the fried sweet bean paste then cover with 4 stewed beef slices and make it a roll, cut it twice to become 3 parts when eating.

麦片粥 / CEREAL CONGEE

● 材料

　　肉馅 75 克、燕麦片 1 杯、大米半杯、盐 1 茶匙、料酒 1 大匙

● 作法

　　1．先用 2 大匙油将肉馅炒散，并淋料酒 1 大匙后炒匀盛出。

　　2．大米洗净，加水 3 杯煮粥，米粒熟软前，倒入燕麦同煮，并加盐调味，最后加入肉末，煮匀即可盛出。

● INGREDIENTS

3oz. ground pork, 1c. cereal, 1/2c. rice, 1t. salt, 1T. cooking wine

● METHODS

1. Stir-fry the ground pork with 2T. oil, add 1T. wine,and mix well.

2. Wash the rice and add 3c. water to make the congee,cook until rice get softened, pour the cereal and cook together, add salt to taste then add the stir-fried ground pork at last, stir well and ready to serve.

重 点 提 示
NOTE

1. 甜面酱 3 大匙、糖 1 大匙，用少许油炒匀，即成抹在饼上之酱料。
2. 超市可买到冷冻葱油饼，或自己做好后放冰箱冷冻再分次使用。

1. Stir-fry 3T. sweet bean paste and 1T.sugar with a bit of oil, then become the paste on the beef roll.
2. You can buy the frozen Chinese pancake in the supermarket, or you can make it by your own for any use.

菜肉包子 + 杏仁茶
MEAT BUNS + ALMOND TEA

● 材料
现成品（视个人食量）

● 作法
食用时回锅加热即可。

● INGREDIENTS
The already-made meat buns(depends on how much the eater can eat)

● METHODS
Steam and serve.

 杏仁茶 / ALMOND TEA

● 材料
杏仁粉半杯、水淀粉 3 大匙、糖半杯

● 作法
1. 将杏仁粉与 2 杯清水调匀，放火上煮开，再加糖调味。
2. 水淀粉在煮开时慢慢淋入，勾芡成薄糊状即可盛出饮用。

● INGREDIENTS
1/2c. almond powder, 3T. cornstarch solution, 1/2c.sugar

● METHODS
1. Mix the almond powder and 2c water well, bring to a boil, add sugar to taste.
2. Pour the cornstarch solution slowly, cook until thicken, then ready to serve.

重 点 提 示
NOTE

如有糯米粉，可代替淀粉勾芡，使杏仁茶口感更滑顺，此味饮料冷热饮皆可。

The cornstarch can be replaced by the sticky rice powder, the taste of almond tea will be more smooth, and this kind of drink is suitable for both hot and cold.

肉末番茄汤 / GROUND PORK AND TOMATO SOUP ◆

● 材料

肉馅75克、番茄3个、香菜少许、盐半茶匙、料酒1大匙、水淀粉1大匙

● 作法

1. 番茄洗净，先氽烫过，将皮剥掉，再切丁；肉馅先用2大匙油爆炒过，并淋料酒1大匙后，加水3杯煮开。

2. 将番茄丁加入汤内同煮，并加盐调味后，慢慢淋入水淀粉勾芡，盛出后再加少许香菜即成。

● INGREDIENTS

5oz. ground pork, 3 tomatoes, coriander as needed,1/2t. salt, 1T. cooking wine, 1T. cornstarch solution

● METHODS

1. Wash, blanch, skin and dice the tomatoes; stir-fry the ground pork with 2T. oil until fragrant, add 1T. wine, then add 3T. water and bring to a boil.

2. Add tomato dices and bring to a boil, add salt to taste, and thicken with cornstarch solution, then add the coriander, ready to serve.

◆ 寿司 / SUSHI

● 材料

米1杯、米醋2大匙、糖2大匙、肉松1杯、小黄瓜1条、海苔片3张

● 作法

1. 米洗净，加水2/3杯，先浸泡20分钟，再入锅煮成饭，趁热加入米醋和糖调匀。

2. 小黄瓜用盐搓洗外皮后，洗净，切成4长条。

3. 将海苔片铺平，放入米饭少许，再铺入肉松和1条小黄瓜，卷紧，再用刀切成小段即成。

● INGREDIENTS

1c. rice, 2T. rice vinegar, 2T. sugar, 1c. dried fried pork, 1 Chinese cucumber, 3 sheets nori dried seaweed

● METHODS

1. Wash rice, add 2/3c. water and soak for 20 minutes, then cook it as a rice, add the rice vinegar and sugar while hot, and mix well.

2. Scratch the cucumber with salt, wash and cut into four strips.

3. Spread the nori seaweed, then spread the rice evenly, sprinkle some dried fried pork and a cucumber strip, roll up tightly, then cut into small pieces.

肉末烧饼 / GROUND PORK WITH ROASTED PANCAKE

● 材料

长形烧饼2个，牛肉馅225克，大蒜3瓣，葱2根，辣椒1个，香菜2棵，料酒1大匙，酱油、水淀粉各少许

● 作法

1．用2大匙油炒牛肉馅，变白时淋料酒1大匙，炒匀先盛出。

2．大蒜、葱、辣椒、香菜分别切碎，用2大匙油先炒香蒜末，再放入牛肉馅，接着加葱末、辣椒末、香菜，并加酱油调味，勾芡后炒匀即盛出。

3．烧饼对切两段，放入烤箱再烤热，约2分钟，然后取出，将切口张开，盛入炒好的肉末即可食用。

● INGREDIENTS

2 long roasted pancake, 1/2lb. ground beef, 3 cloves garlic, 2 scallions, 1 chili pepper, 2 stalks coriander, 1T. cooking wine, soy sauce, corn starch solution as needed

● METHODS

1. Stir-fry the ground beef with 2T. oil until color changes, add wine and stir well.

2. Chop the garlic, scallions, chili pepper and coriander. Stir-fry the chopped garlic with 2T. oil until fragrant, then add the ground beef, chopped scallions, chopped chili peppers and coriander, add all seasonings to taste, mix well.

3. Cut the roasted pancake in halves, heat up in the oven for 2 minutes, remove, open the cutting edge and stuff in the beef mixture. Ready to serve.

◆ 豆浆 / SOYBEAN MILK

● 材料

黄豆300克、糖1杯

● 作法

黄豆洗净，用水浸泡4小时，然后用榨汁机打碎，沥出浆汁后，煮开，加糖调味即可。

● INGREDIENTS

2/3lb. soybeans, 1c. sugar

● METHODS

Rinse soybeans, soak in water for 4 hours, then put into a blender, liquidize and bring to a boil, add sugar to taste. Ready to serve.

皮蛋瘦肉粥 + 发糕

PRESERVED EGG AND PORK CONGEE + CANTONESE SPONGE CAKE

● 材料

大米2杯，皮蛋2个，瘦肉150克，葱花、香菜各少许，盐1茶匙，酱油、淀粉各少许

● 作法

1．大米洗净，加水8杯煮成粥，皮蛋去壳、切片，瘦肉切碎粒并拌人少许酱油和淀粉，待粥煮沸时加人皮蛋和瘦肉煮匀。

2．加盐调味，并撒人葱花和香菜，即可盛出食用。

● INGREDIENTS

2c. rice, 2 preserved eggs, 5oz. lean pork, chopped scallions as needed, coriander as needed, 1T. salt, dash of soy sauce, a pinch of cornstarch

● METHODS

1. Wash the rice, add 8c. water and make the congee; Shell and slice the preserved eggs; mince the lean pork and marinate with soy sauce and cornstarch,after the congee boil, add the preserved egg and lean pork and mix well.

2. Add salt to taste, sprinkle on the chopped scallions and coriander and ready to serve.

◆ 发糕 / CANTONESE SPONGE CAKE

● 材料

鸡蛋5个、中筋面粉2杯、糖1杯、玻璃纸1张

● 作法

1．将蛋白、蛋黄分开，蛋白打发，再拌人糖及色拉油打匀，慢慢筛人面粉，调成面糊。

2．蒸笼内铺一张玻璃纸，再将面糊倒人，锅内水烧开，将蒸笼放人，大火蒸40分钟，取出后放凉，切小块即可食用。

● INGREDIENTS

5 eggs,2c.all-purpose flour,1c.sugar,1 sheet cellophane wrap

● METHODS

1. Separate the egg white and egg yolk, beat the egg white until fluffy, add sugar and oil and mix well, slowly pour into the flour and stir well to make the batter.

2. Spread the cellophone wrap in the steamer, then pour down the batter in, boil the water in the pot, put into the steamer, and steam with high heat for 40 minutes, then remove and let cool, cut into small pieces and ready to serve.

重点提示 NOTE

发糕可以买现成品代替，食用前蒸热即可。

It can be also replaced by the already-made products, heat up befor eating.

杯子蛋糕 / CUP CAKE

● 材料

低筋面粉 1 杯、小苏打粉 1/4 茶匙、发粉半茶匙、鸡蛋 1 个

● 调味料

（1）细砂糖半杯、香草片 1 片

（2）油 2 大匙、奶半杯

● 作法

1. 将低筋面粉、小苏打粉和发粉混合过筛，并将香草片碾碎；鸡蛋打散，加入调味料(1)和(2)拌匀，再慢慢加入筛过的面粉，调匀成糊状。

2. 在小杯子内先放 1 张模型纸，再倒入面糊八分满，放入烤箱，在 180℃烤 20 分钟。

3. 取出后再将模型纸扣出即成。

● INGREDIENTS

1c. cake flour, 1/4T. baking soda, 1/2T. baking powder, 1egg

● SEASONINGS

(1) 1/2c. sugar, 1 piece vanilla

(2) 2T. oil, 1/2c.milk

● METHODS

1. Mix flour, baking soda and baking powder together, sift; grind vanilla Beat egg, add the seasoning (1)and (2) and stir finely, slowly pour down the flour, and stir well to form a batter.

2. Place a mold paper in the small cup , then pour down the batter into the cup , place in the oven and bake at 180℃ for 20 minutes.

3. Remove cup cakes and ready to serve.

杂粮粥 / WHOLEWHEAT CONGEE

● 材料

杂粮 2 杯(包括大麦、小麦、荞麦、薏仁、麦片，或其他不同种类的粮食和豆类)

● 作法

1. 杂粮洗净，泡 3 小时，再加清水 12 杯煮开。

2. 改小火，熬至米粒熟烂时即可关火食用。

● INGREDIENTS

2c. wholewheat rice (include barleey,wheat, buckwheat, pearl barley or different kinds of wholewheats)

● METHODS

1. Wash the rice and soak in water for 3 hours, then add 12c. water and bring to boil.

2. Reduce heat to low,cook until the rice gets softened, then remove from heat and ready to eat.

韭菜蒸饺 + 紫米粥

STEAMED CHINESE CHIVE DUMPLINGS + PURPLE SWEET RICE CONGEE

韭菜蒸饺 / STEAMED CHINESE CHIVE DUMPLINGS

● 材料

肉馅 150 克、韭菜 150 克、粉丝 1 把、盐半茶匙、香油 3 大匙、饺子皮 75 克、料酒 1 大匙

● 作法

1. 肉馅先用 2 大匙油炒香，并淋料酒 1 大匙后盛出。另将韭菜洗净、切碎，拌入肉馅及泡软、切碎的粉丝。

2. 加盐和香油调味后做成馅料，在每张饺子皮中包入馅料少许，捏紧，放蒸笼内，大火蒸 5 分钟，取出即可食用。

重点提示 NOTE

蒸饺的皮本应用烫面擀成，此处为求快速便捷，故改用现成饺子皮。

The dumpling wrappers supposed to made of the pastry, here is the quick and fast way to cook, therefore we can use already-made dumpling wrappers.

● INGREDIENTS

5oz. ground pork, 5oz. chinese chive, 1 bundle mung bean noodles, 1/2T. salt, 3T. sesame oil, 3oz dumpling wrappers, 1T. cooking wine

● METHODS

1. Stir-fry the ground pork with 2T. oil until fragrant and add wine, then add washed and chopped Chinese chive ,add the ground pork and softened and chopped mung bean noodles.

2. Add salt and sesame oil to make the filling, put some filling into each wrapper, seal tightly, put into a steamer, steam over high heat for 5 minutes, remove and ready to serve.

◆ 紫米粥 / PURPLE SWEET RICE CONGEE

● 材料

黑糯米 2 杯、糖 1 杯

● 作法

1. 黑糯米洗净，加水 15 杯浸泡 2 小时，再移至火上煮开，改小火熬煮至熟烂。

2. 加糖调味后即可食用。

● INGREDIENTS

2c. black sticky rice, 1c. sugar

● METHODS

1. Wash rice, add 15c. water and soak for 2 hours, bring to a boil, then reduce heat to low, and simmering until getting softened.

2. Add sugar to taste and ready to serve.

重点提示 NOTE

这道粥需时较久，不妨提前煮好，例如前一天晚上熬好，食用时再取适量加热，亦可吃凉的。

This congee takes a long time to cook, so it is suggested that you can cook in advance. For example: You can make the congee the night before, heat up the amout that you prefer, it is also nice for cold dish.

果酱土司 + 鲜果西米露
TOAST WITH JAM + FRUIT TAPIOCA

● 材料

土司2片、果酱酌量

● 作法

1. 土司用烤面包机烤至酥黄取出。
2. 抹上各自喜欢的果酱或花生酱，或奶油皆可。

● INGREDIENTS

2 pieces toasts, jam as needed

● METHODS

1. Toast the toasts with the toaster until golden brown on both sides
2. It can be optional to spread on the jam, peanut butter and butter.

 鲜果西米露 / FRUIT TAPIOCA

● 材料

西米1杯、椰浆1罐、白糖1杯、新鲜水果酌量

● 作法

1. 水半锅烧开，放入西米煮5分钟，半透明时捞出。
2. 椰浆倒入锅内，加水1杯煮开，加糖调味，煮匀后关火，再放入煮好的西米拌匀。食用时盛出少许，加入切成小块的各类新鲜水果即成。

● INGREDIENTS

1c. tapioca,1c an of coconut milk,1c.sugar,fresh fruit as needed

● METHODS

1. Boil half pot of the water, put the tapioca to cook until opaque for 5 minutes, remove.
2. Pour the coconut milk into the pot, add 1c.water and bring to a boi add sugar to taste, stir well, remove from heat, and add cooked tapi oca and stir well. Take some out when you're eating, the add some diced fresh fruits. Ready to serve.

炒米粉 + 肉丸汤
STIR-FRIED RICE NOODLES + MEATBALL SOUP

● 材料

新鲜米粉300克、熟肉臊半杯、豆芽75克、韭菜5根、酱油3大匙、盐半茶匙

● 作法

1. 先用2大匙油炒洗净的豆芽和切成小段的韭菜，炒熟盛出。

2. 另用2大匙油，烧热，加入酱油、盐、清水1杯烧开，放入米粉拌炒至入味，待汤汁收干时，倒入豆芽和韭菜，拌匀即盛出。

3. 最后淋上熟肉臊即可食用。

● INGREDIENTS

2/3lb. rice noodles, 1/2c. stewed ground pork, 3oz. bean sprouts, 5 stalks Chinese chive, 3T. soy sauce, 1/2t. salt

● METHODS

1. Stir-fry cleaned bean sprouts and Chinese chive sections with 2T. oil until done, remove.

2. Heat 2T. oil, add soy sauce, salt and 1c.water and bring to boil, add rice nodles and cook until the flavor is absorbed, add bean sprouts and Chinese chive, mix well.

3. Sprinkle some stewed ground pork and ready to serve.

熟肉臊作法是先将五花肉绞碎，用5大匙油炒香葱花后，加入肉馅同炒，并拌入泡软、切碎的香菇末后，加少许酒、酱油、糖、五香粉调味，并加水一同熬煮而成，最好先做好，随时取用才方便。

Make the stewed ground pork-Mince the pork. Stir-fry with 5T. oil with some dried shallots until fragrant, add pork and the softened and chopped mushrooms, add wine, soy sauce, sugar and five-spice powder to taste. add some water and stew for a while. It is suggested that make the stewed minced meat in advance for any use.

肉丸汤 / MEATBALL SOUP

● 材料

肉丸4粒、番茄1个、小黄瓜1条、盐半茶匙

● 作法

1. 将肉丸切十字刀口，放入煮开的3杯水内，并将番茄洗净、切片放入，最后放入洗净切好的小黄瓜片同煮。

2. 待沸，加盐调味即成。

● INGREDIENTS

4 meatballs, 1 tomato, 1 Chinese cucumber, 1/2t. salt

● METHODS

1. Cut across the meatball on surface, put into the 3c. boiling water, then add washed and sliced tomato, add the sliced cucumber to cook together.

2. Add salt to taste when it is boiling.

炒米粉 + 肉丸汤

葱油饼 + 藕粉茶
SCALLION PANCAKE + LILY ROOT POWDER TEA

材料
中筋面粉 2 杯、葱 3 根、猪油 5 大匙、盐 1 茶匙

作法
1. 中筋面粉放盆内，冲入开水 2 杯及少许冷水后，揉匀成面团，放置 10 分钟。

2. 葱洗净、切碎，醒好的面团先拌入 2 大匙猪油揉匀，然后擀成大片，再抹上猪油，撒上切好的葱花和盐之后，卷成筒状，盘好再擀开。

3. 将擀好的面片用平底锅以少许油煎至两面金黄即可盛出，切小片食用。

INGREDIENTS
2c. all purpose flour, 3 scallions, 5T. lard, 1t. salt

METHODS
1. Put flour into a mixing bowl, pour 2c. boiling water and some cold water, mix and knead to make a dough, and set aside for 10 minutes.

2. Wash and chop the scallions, add 2T. lard and mix with the dough, then roll it into a big piece. Spread on 3T. lard, chopped scallions and salt, roll up, roll it like a snail and roll out like a round cake.

3. Fry round cake with some oil in the fry pan until golden brown on both sides, cut it into small pieces and serve.

重点提示 NOTE

葱油饼亦可做成小张，一次多做些，冷藏再分次取用，或直接选购成品，食用前再加热。

You can also make the smaller size scallion pancake, make more in one time and store them in the freezer for any use, or buy the already-made products directly, fry them before eating.

藕粉茶 / LILY ROOT POWDER TEA

材料
藕粉 2 大匙、细白糖 2 大匙

作法
藕粉放杯内，连同细白糖先用少许冷开水稀释，调匀后冲入沸水，调匀即可饮用。

INGREDIENTS
2T. lily root powder, 2T. sugar

METHODS
Pour some lotus powder into the cup, dissolve altogether with sugar with cold water, mix and add some boiling water then serve

葱油饼 + 藕粉茶

SCALLION PANCAKE + LILY ROOT POWDER TEA

葱蛋馒头 + 豆浆
SCALLIONS AND EGG BUNS + SOYBEAN MILK

● 材料

馒头2个、葱2根、鸡蛋1个、盐半茶匙

● 作法

1. 馒头用刀横切成3片，放入电锅蒸热备用。

2. 葱洗净、切碎，加入打散的蛋液中，并加盐调味后，用平底锅以少许油煎成葱花蛋。

3. 在锅内用锅铲将蛋切小块，再夹入馒头中即可食用。

● INGREDIENTS

2 buns, 2 scallions,1 egg, 1/2t.salt

● METHODS

1. Cut the bun into 3 pieces, steam in the rice cooker.

2. Wash and chop scallions, add to the beaten egg, add salt to taste fry egg mixture with a bit of oil until like a omlette.

3. Cut the egg omlette into small pieces, the stuff in the buns, then ready to serve.

豆浆 / SOYBEAN MILK

● 材料

黄豆300克、糖1杯

● 作法

黄豆洗净，用水浸泡4小时，然后用榨汁机打碎，滤出浆汁后，煮开，加糖调味即可。

● INGREDIENTS

2/3lb. soybeans, 1c. sugar

● METHODS

Rinse soybeans,soak in water for 4 hours, then put into a blender, liquidize and bring to a boil, add sugar to taste. Ready to serve.

芋头咸粥
SALTY TARO CONGEE

● 材料

芋头1个、大米2杯、芹菜1根、虾米2大匙、盐1茶匙

● 作法

1. 芋头去皮、洗净、切丁；大米洗净，加水10杯先浸泡20分钟；芹菜洗净，切丁。

2. 将大米煮开后，改小火熬粥。

3. 另用3大匙油爆香泡软的虾米，放入芋头丁炒过，再倒入粥内同煮。

4. 待芋头及米粒皆已熟软时，加盐调味，最后放入芹菜末拌匀，即可盛出食用。

● INGREDIENTS

1 taro , 2c. rice, 1 stick Chinese celery, 2T. dried shrimps, 1t. salt

● METHODS

1. Skin, wash and dice taro; wash rice,then add 10c. water to soak fo 20 minutes; wash and dice the celery.

2. Boil the rice, then keep simmering the congee with over low heat.

3. Srir-fry the softened shrimps with 3T. oil, then add the diced taro and stir well, add into the congee and keep boiling.

4. Wait until the taro and rice get softened, add salt to taste,then add the chopped celery, stir well and ready to serve.

法国土司 + 麦乳精
FRENCH TOAST + MALTED MILK

● 材料

土司 3 片、鲜奶 1 杯、鸡蛋 1 个、细白糖少许

● 作法

1. 土司修去四边硬皮，对切三角形。
2. 鸡蛋打散，加入鲜奶调匀，每片土司沾上一层牛奶蛋液后，放入平底锅，用少许油将土司两面煎黄即可盛出。
3. 在煎好的土司上撒少许细白糖即可食用 (不加亦可)。

● INGREDIENTS

3 pieces toasts,1c. milk, 1 egg, sugar as needed

● METHODS

1. Cut the rim of the toasts, then cut into the 2 triangles.
2. Beat egg, mix with the milk, dip the milk and egg mixture onto each toast, and put it into the fryer pan, then saute the toasts golden brown on both sides with a bit of oil.
3. Spread some sugars onto the toasts and ready to serve.

 麦乳精 / MALTED MILK

● 材料

麦乳精 2 大匙、糖半大匙

● 作法

1. 麦乳精放杯内，同时将糖放入。
2. 加入开水，调匀即可饮用。

● INGREDIENTS

2T. malted milk, 1/2T. sugar

● METHODS

1. Pour the malted milk powder into the cup, then add the sugar in at the same time.
2. Add the boiling water, then ready to serve.

干拌面 + 紫菜蛋花汤
DRY NOODLE + LAVER AND EGG SOUP

● 材料
鸡蛋细面1束、葱末1茶匙
● 调味料
黑醋1大匙、酱油半大匙、橄榄油1大匙、香油半茶匙
● 作法
1. 先将半锅水烧开(约3杯),放入细面煮熟。
2. 面碗内先放入葱末及所有调味料拌匀。
3. 将煮好的细面捞出放入,拌匀即可。

● INGREDIENTS
1 bunch egg noodles, 1t. chopped scallions
● SEASONINGS
1T. black vinegar, 1/2T. soy sauce, 1T. olive oil, 1/2t. sesame oil
● METHODS
1. Bring half pot of water to a boil (3c.), add moodle to cook until done. Drain and set aside.
2. Put chopped scallions and all seasonings to a serving bowl, stir well.
3. Add cooked noodle, mix well and serve.

◆ 紫菜蛋花汤 / LAVER AND EGG SOUP

● 材料
鸡蛋1个、紫菜2张、葱1根
● 调味料
盐半茶匙、香油少许
● 作法
1. 2杯水放小锅中煮开,将鸡蛋打散淋入,并加盐调味,煮至蛋凝成蛋花即关火。
2. 将紫菜撕成小片,葱洗净、切碎一并放入,滴入香油少许,即可盛入碗内食用。

● INGREDIENTS
1 egg, 2 sheets dry laver, 1 scallion
● SEASONINGS
1/2t. salt, few drops sesame oil
● METHODS
1. Bring 2c. water to a boil; beat egg and pour into the boiling water then add salt to taste, cook until the egg done, remove from heat.
2. Tear laver into small pieces; rinse and chop scallion. Add both to the soup from method (1), and drop few sesame oil. Serve.

NOTE

1. 除了鸡蛋细面也可以用其他细面,或视各人喜好选用,新鲜面条较易煮;若用干面条,煮的时间要较长才能软烂。
2. 紫菜易熟软,故不宜太早加入,以免太烂。

1. Besides egg noodles, other noodles are optional to individual preference. Fresh noodles take little to be boiled; ready-made noodles take much.
2. Don't put the laver to the boiling soup too early, or it will be like paste.

干拌面 + 紫菜蛋花汤

图书在版编目(CIP)数据

营养早餐 / 梁琼白著. —北京：中国轻工业出版社，2002.8（2004.1 重印）
（现代人食谱）
ISBN 7－5019－3746－X

Ⅰ．营…　Ⅱ．梁…　Ⅲ．保健－食谱　Ⅳ.TS972.161

中国版本图书馆 CIP 数据核字（2002）第 049922 号

版权声明
　　原书名：營養早餐
　　作　者：梁瓊白
　　© 台湾膳書房文化事業有限公司　1998
　　本书中文简体版本由台湾膳书房文化事业有限公司授权出版

责任编辑：施　纪　高惠京　　责任终审：滕炎福　　封面设计：赵小云
版式设计：张　颖　　　　　　责任校对：燕　杰　　责任监印：吴京一
*
出版发行：中国轻工业出版社（北京东长安街 6 号，邮编：100740）
印　　刷：北京百花彩印有限公司
经　　销：各地新华书店
版　　次：2002 年 8 月第 1 版　　2004 年 1 月第 3 次印刷
开　　本：889 × 1194　1/24　印张：3.5
字　　数：76 千字
书　　号：ISBN 7－5019－3746－X / TS ·2227
定　　价：18.00 元
著作权合同登记　图字：01-2002-2710
读者服务部邮购热线电话：010－65241695　85111729　传真：85111730
发行电话：010－88390721　88390722
网　　址：http://www.chlip.com.cn
Email：club@chlip.com.cn

如发现图书残缺请直接与我社读者服务部联系调换
30939SIC105ZYW